PHEWW!!

Elisha, the brothers and the fantastically full jars

Bob Hartman

Illustrations by Emma Hagan

CWR

For Malachi and Jacob

This story is found in
2 Kings 4:1-7

Hi!
My name's Josh.
And this is my little brother Jake.

He does everything I do.

Like climbing trees.

And chasing rock badgers.

My mum says he's my shadow.

Which is kind of annoying.
Except ... I would miss
my shadow if he wasn't there.

And maybe, real soon, he won't be.

So they told her they were going to take **me and Jake** and sell us as slaves.

He's a prophet, which sort of means that God talks to him sometimes.

My dad was a prophet, too. Elisha was his boss.

Mum thinks that maybe God can use Elisha to help us.

Hang on, she's calling us. **Be right back.**

You tell me if this sounds crazy to you.

Elisha said that me and Jake should go into the village, borrow as many empty jars and jugs as we can find and bring them back to the house.

He says God has a plan .

Mum says that Elisha told her to take the last little bit of olive oil she has and pour it into one of the jugs.

Did you see that?

But Mum says we can sell the oil to raise the money we need.

God has saved us!

And now we don't need to be sold as slaves. Not me. Not Jake.

And you know what that means, don't you?

Gulp

Look out for more Talking Tales ...
YUMMM!! – Elijah, the boy and the amazing famine feast
SHHHH!! – Miriam, the baby and the secret basket boat
ZZZZZ!! – Samuel, the night and the curious calling voice